Gomez
Bring It On

International MUSIC Publications

INTERNATIONAL MUSIC PUBLICATIONS LIMITED

ENGLAND: GRIFFIN HOUSE,
161 HAMMERSMITH ROAD, LONDON W6 8BS
GERMANY: MARSTALLSTR. 8. D-80539 MUNCHEN
DENMARK: DANMUSIK, VOGNMAGERGADE 7
DK 1120 KOBENHAVNK

WARNER/CHAPPELL MUSIC

CANADA: 40 SHEPPARD AVE. WEST, SUITE 800
TORONTO, ONTARIO M2N 6K9
SCANDINAVIA: P.O. BOX 533, VENDEVAGEN 85 B
S-182 15, DANDERYD, SWEDEN
AUSTRALIA: P.O. BOX 353
3 TALAVERA ROAD, NORTH RYDE N.S.W. 2113

Nuova CARISH S.p.A.

ITALY: VIA CAMPANIA, 12
20098 S. GIULIANO MILANESE (MI)
ZONA INDUSTRIALE SESTO ULTERIANO
FRANCE: 20, RUE DE LA VILLE-L'EVEQUE,
75008 PARIS

WARNER BROS. PUBLICATIONS
THE GLOBAL LEADER IN PRINT

USA: 15800 NW 48TH AVENUE
MIAMI, FL 33014

Music Transcribed by Barnes Music Engraving Ltd., East Sussex TN22 4HA
Printed by The Panda Group · Haverhill · Suffolk CB9 8PR · UK · Suffolk Bound · Ipswich

Official Band Photo, Scarlet Page. Other Photos, S.F.

Those present   Ian Ball, Paul Blackburn, Tom Gray, Ben Ottewell, Olly Peacock, Rebecca Elson, Steve Fellows

S.F.	That is definitely on and working…
Olly	Blackie could do the Barry White thing….

(laughter)

S.F.	O.K.
Blackie	….got a great one of those…
S.F.	Back in time… back in time *(in bad U.S. accent)*
Blackie	Blake Snake Pliskin!
S.F.	GET MILES…

(mobile phone rings, everyone begins to sing along to the tune it plays)

Hello?… Hello?…

Tape Stops, Tape Starts again, (Rustling sound)

BEN	It was a blues song, then it went quite rocky *(sings)* so then it was a rock song which went… *(sings again)*
OLLY	then Tom went *(imitates sound of octave intro. part)*
BEN	then Oll' put the tongue drum on… and it become a groovy song, and now it's a rock song again.
IAN	the original riff ended up at the end of the line version of '78
BEN	It's pretty much a riff you can play with any song
IAN	yeah
BLACKIE	then Mr Q (Mat Quinton - tuba) did his magic
IAN	then we turned a tuba into an entire brass section with studio gimmickry
BEN	….weaving voodoo spells
IAN	a heady brew with tubic nonsense…

(laughs like Vincent Price)

BEN	tuberous
TOM	tuberous soul!
OLLY	the drum machine and all that wasn't it?
BEN	that goes *(sings)* 'Once upon a time…'
TOM	I had an old drum machine from the 1980's and we'd been messing around with it over the summer in a dirty old garage and Ian had that song which was written about the famous Beck gig… and we got into his conservatory and we spent a very drunken night putting it all together.
BEN	very, very drunk
TOM	yes, we were very drunk
BEN	….very, very
TOM	And that's how that song came into being
BEN	….there was a xylophone
TOM	oh yes, there was an old xylophone
BEN	it was me and Oll'
IAN	I was holding it
S.F.	a three man xylophone part
BEN	very good
IAN	I hurt my hand after a while
BEN	there's slide guitar on it as well
	MAKE NO SOUND
BEN	that was written in Ian's house after I'd screwed up 'Touchin' up'… and everyone had… no-one was there… everyone had fucked off in disgust and outrage.
TOM	I went home for my tea
OLLY	I went home for my tea as well
TOM	I went home for my tea then came back after dinner
OLLY	then we came back and we were like.. yeah?
BEN	but then we had a song so it made it alright
TOM & OLLY *(in unison)*	yeah
IAN	it was written in about 10 seconds flat
S.F.	I've got something here which says it's about Ian's relationship with his dogs
BEN	the dog is like the 'he's fine', that's Ian's dog - and Ian's the 'she' and it's about the dog telling him… erm… (undecipherable)
TOM	It's a good story, the bit, er… 'cos what's… how, how we found…
BEN	Ian Bracken (cello player on M.N.S.)
TOM	Yes, 'cos you rang up that guy from the Auteurs
BEN	Yeah, that's quite a good story… then he said 'I can't do it… use my mate'
S.F.	It's not the best story I've ever heard
TOM	but that's how we found him
BEN	but that's good though… Auteurs
IAN	The notes were on a cigarette packet, so that shows you how many notes are involved in the cello line
BEN	Five
IAN	Five notes
BEN	G, D, A, E,… no, it's… yeah, G, D, A, E,
IAN	Three notes
BEN	G, D, A… there's a C in there as well
	78 STONE WOBBLE
OLLY	Yeah
IAN	L'ascenseur du sh… scaffold
BEN	Oll' likes jazz
TOM	lift to the scaffold… lift to the scaffold
BEN	Oll' wouldn't do it, man… it's a good drum beat that though
IAN	sound drum beat at the back
TOM	nice back beat
OLLY	it's 'cos Noel Redding told me to use it…
TOM	in a dream…
BEN	Noel Redding told him to use brushes on that track
IAN	in a dream…
OLLY	and he made me track it
IAN	that's a good sign… nice dream about Noel Redding
BEN	Oll' had a dream, like the night before we did the track
IAN	Noel Redding visited him
BEN	Noel Redding appeared and told him to play the brushes the following day
	TIJUANA LADY
IAN	I woke up one morning and started playing the guitar and Ben started singing
BEN	then Blackie wrote all the words
S.F.	did you?
BLACKIE	no
BEN	he wrote the chorus
IAN	yeah, coming back from a stoned trip to the woods… I remember
BEN	In the woods?
IAN	yeah, yeah, the woods, by Hillside
TOM	Woods, man, that's a wood
BEN	That's not a wood… that's a…
TOM	Is it not a clear wood?
BEN	full of trees
IAN	by Hillside, that's a clear wood
BEN	arse!
BLACKIE	it's a forest
IAN	it's a forest in fact
BLACKIE	it's a forest in Hillside
TOM	two trees
IAN	there's more than two
BEN	we went and had a smoke in two trees?
IAN	there's clearly more than two… it's a forest
BECKA	it's actual name is Hillside forest
BEN	you're kidding
TOM	bollocks, it's really not the size of a hill
BEN	it's not even a fucking hill
TOM	Hillside
BECKA	it's a mountain
IAN	it's a forest on a mountain
BEN	it's a mound
S.F.	alright… that's enough about 'Tijuana'

BEN	we went to 'moundside trees'
IAN	no, no, we went to mountainside forest and walked back to Blackie's house
BEN	Mountainside rainforest.. trekked... trekked all the way through
BLACKIE	to my... er... mountainside shack
IAN	then we completely destroyed the song using that secret...
BEN	using the secrets of the ancients...
TOM	using the old music
IAN	the old one-two
TOM	my Grandma's old Dansette
BEN	That was Cher's idea that one, yeah, it was Cher... Cher appeared as if by magic in Ian's back garden and told us to play it that slow...

(all begin to sing Cher's recent big hit)

HERE COMES THE BREEZE

TOM	the second part of that was originally a song called 'Collapse'
IAN	it was a way of getting from E to B
BEN	via the art of G
IAN	we played that section for about 20 hours after a Black Crowes gig, we played it in 2 keys
BEN	with no drugs in our bodies
IAN	not a SAUSAGE
BEN	no acid or speed
IAN	and there's something about a backwards melody which...
BEN	yeah
IAN	became the 'Tijuana'... that melody...
BEN	melody
IAN	backwards is the verse melody for 'Tijuana'
S.F.	but which came first?
IAN	we don't really know.. it's one of those egg/chicken type events
BEN	chicken

LOVE IS BETTER THAN A WARM TROMBONE

OLLY	You'd had that hanging around for a while
TOM	I'd had the chords and the melody and I finished the words on the train back to the studio
OLLY	We did it really quickly in the studio
TOM	we recorded it at the end of the session
IAN	Oh, and you played a really good bit on it, stone
S.F.	I did, didn't I?

(Ian sings Fuzz guitar part)

BEN	what was your inspiration behind that guitar?
S.F.	Er,... I don't know... what was it... it was
BEN	what were you trying to express?
S.F.	Violence... anger... angularity... exploiting what you could do with that 4 chord swing, y'know.

GET MYSELF ARRESTED

TOM	Alison (*Donald - Warner/Chappell*) heard it and said it could be in that film. Then we decided it was too good
BEN	Dave Boyd (*M.D. - Hut Recordings*) didn't like it
OLLY	he thought it was a pansy tune
BEN	yeah
OLLY	so we put guitars on
BEN	lots of guitars... and then he liked it
IAN	and the incredible Dobro steel drum
	(Back of steel-bodied Dobro guitar was used as part of percussion)
TOM	and the original guitar line was a bad attempt to sound like Beethoven
BEN	it's about Ian's first pet
IAN	it's not about my first pet, ...that's 'Make No Sound'
BEN	No, but that's about your dog's at the moment... this one's about your first one... first animal
IAN	it was very straight originally then the bass line changed it totally
BEN	put a bigger engine in
IAN	from being straight to being a shuffle
TOM	the bass line was written here (*Parr St. Studio, Liverpool*) that night sitting in someone's bedroom
IAN	then we recorded it the next day

FREE TO RUN

BEN	that's the first song I wrote... that's about it
OLLY	that was the first one I heard you doing
TOM	it was one of the last ones we recorded
IAN	I've got a demo of that with Sims playing congas on it
TOM	No... I'm not saying its...
OLLY	it was inspired by that...
BEN	How do you know?
OLLY	it might be inspired by that
BEN	(lying) I played the drums on that
IAN	it's not as good as the demo with Sims on bongos... masterful bongo part from Sims on that... ga-dunk, ga-dunk ga-dunk, ga-dunk...
IAN	nobody has any idea how to play that song any more. I don't think... I don't know what I tuned my guitar to
OLLY	I know exactly what I played
BEN	yeah, we put a xylophone on that
OLLY	xylophone, yeah
S.F.	I remember a review saying it sounded like a cross between the Beach Boys and a New Orleans funeral
TOM	a lot of 'Pet Sounds' being listened to... actually we were listening to Van Dyke Parks and Brian...
S.F.	yeah, 'Orange Crate Art'
TOM	that first track
IAN	then there's some really good guitar which you can't hear that me and you did on it. All that crazy Flamenco shit... should have turned it up... never mind... next time

RIE'S WAGON

TOM	That's a silly story.. that started with me and Andy.. used to have a bass riff. He did a high part and I played the low part... We played the bass together
BECKA	on the same bass?
TOM	then Ian took the bass part back to Sheffield and the next time I saw him he'd written a song about - around that bass part
IAN	yeah... the version on the album is the... is it the third go we had at recording it?
TOM	it's the third go
BEN	no, it's not, it's the second go... we changed the verse
IAN	no, there were two versions, there were the two four-track versions and the eight track which is the one that survived
TOM	and we played a gig in Norwich, what's that about?
IAN	and we never got the slide as good as we did on the first demo
BEN	we blew up the Squier amp... it was just in the right state of crapness at the time... it went bad... and we managed to fix it and it never sounded as good
S.F.	I remember you getting an amazing sound out of Fender Twins but you could only play the song once - it kept killing them off.. expensive song to perform
BEN	I played it with a can of Pledge as a slide once
S.F.	Oh yeah, couldn't find your slide
BEN	I gave Fish (*Paul Allen - gtr tech*) my slide to look after, and he handed me a bottle of Pledge
OLLY	the arts centre
BEN	it was the one where you and Sarah and Jo had just come back
IAN	Colchester
S.F.	'Cos I saw that, and I didn't go Colchester
OLLY	It was definitely Colchester
BEN	There was a huge pillar in front of the stage
IAN	ah, ...memories.

Get Miles

Words and Music by
Ian Ball, Paul Blackburn, Thomas Gray
Ben Ottewell and Oliver Peacock

1. I love this is-land, but this is-land's kill-ing me.
2. I love this ci-ty man, but this ci-ty's kill-ing me.
3. I love this pla-net, but this pla-net's kill-ing me.

Jump off this is - land, gon-na head out to-wards the sea.
Gon-na leave this ci - ty man, gon-na
Gon-na leave this pla - net man, gon-na

head out to-wards the sea. Get miles a - way, get
head to the ga - la - xy.

miles a - way, get miles a - way, get miles.

to Coda

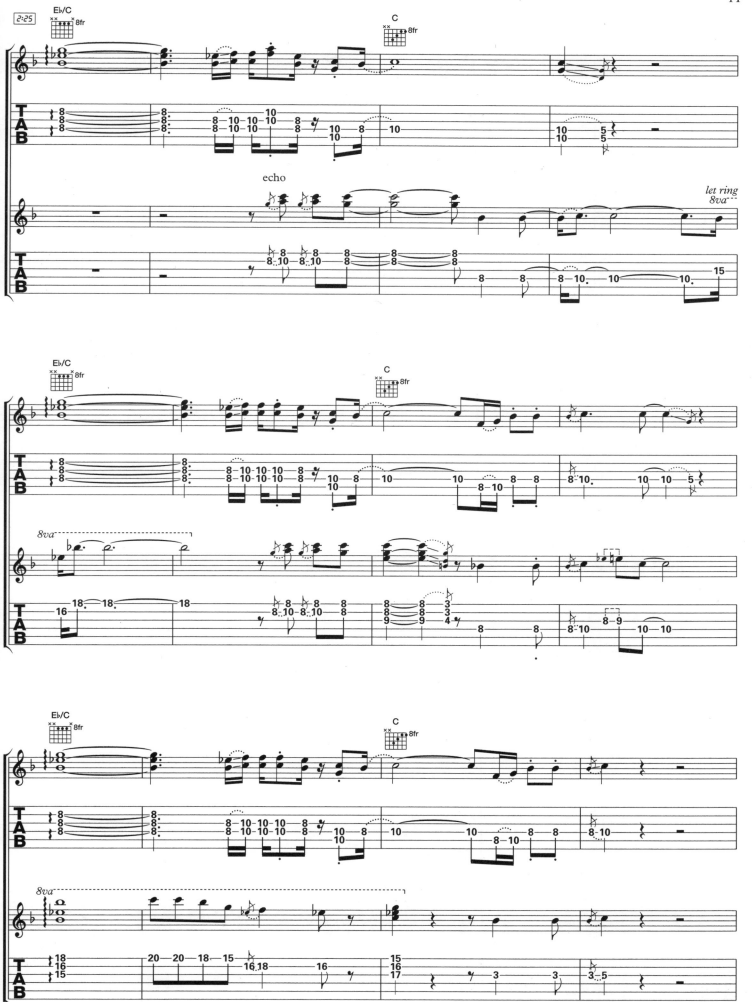

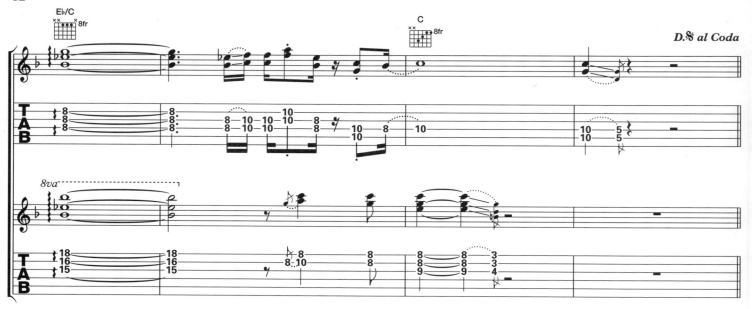

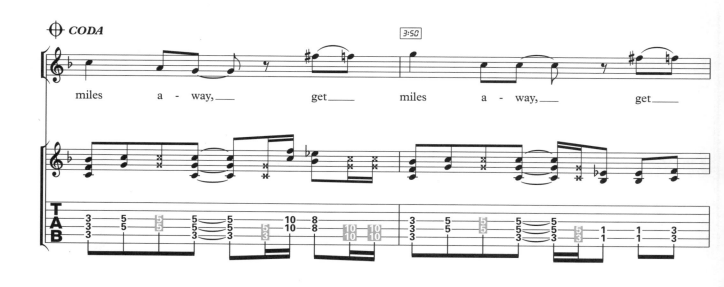

Whippin' Piccadilly

Words and Music by
Ian Ball, Paul Blackburn, Thomas Gray
Ben Ottewell and Oliver Peacock

_(2.)_-mem - ber see - ing some - one dressed in a suit,_ look - ing like a lu - na - tic._

Once up - on a time not_ too long a - go, we took a day_ out_ in Man -

3. Fi - nally made our way back to the train,_ roll - in' in - to Shef-field to - night.

Make No Sound

Words and Music by
Ian Ball, Paul Blackburn, Thomas Gray
Ben Ottewell and Oliver Peacock

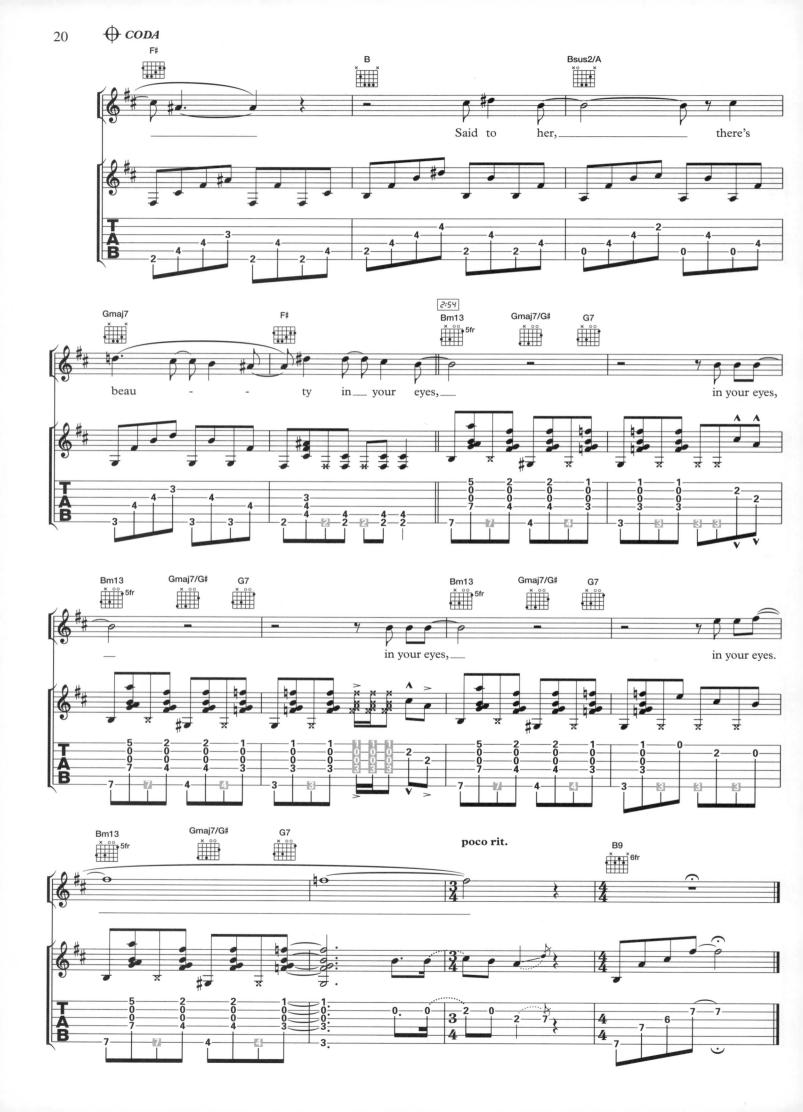

78 Stone Wobble

Words and Music by
Ian Ball, Paul Blackburn, Thomas Gray
Ben Ottewell and Oliver Peacock

1.2. I was al-ways told that you had to have the balls to break down.

Now I'm old - er I'm not so sure.___ I was once told that you had to have the high to low

_ down. An ex - pert told me back in the war.___

Op - en heart - ed sur - gery ne - ver works. ___

Tijuana Lady

Words and Music by
Ian Ball, Paul Blackburn, Thomas Gray
Ben Ottewell and Oliver Peacock

love you, so come back, be with me____ a - gain,____ ah. ____

repeat to fade

Here Comes The Breeze

Words and Music by
Ian Ball, Paul Blackburn, Thomas Gray
Ben Ottewell and Oliver Peacock

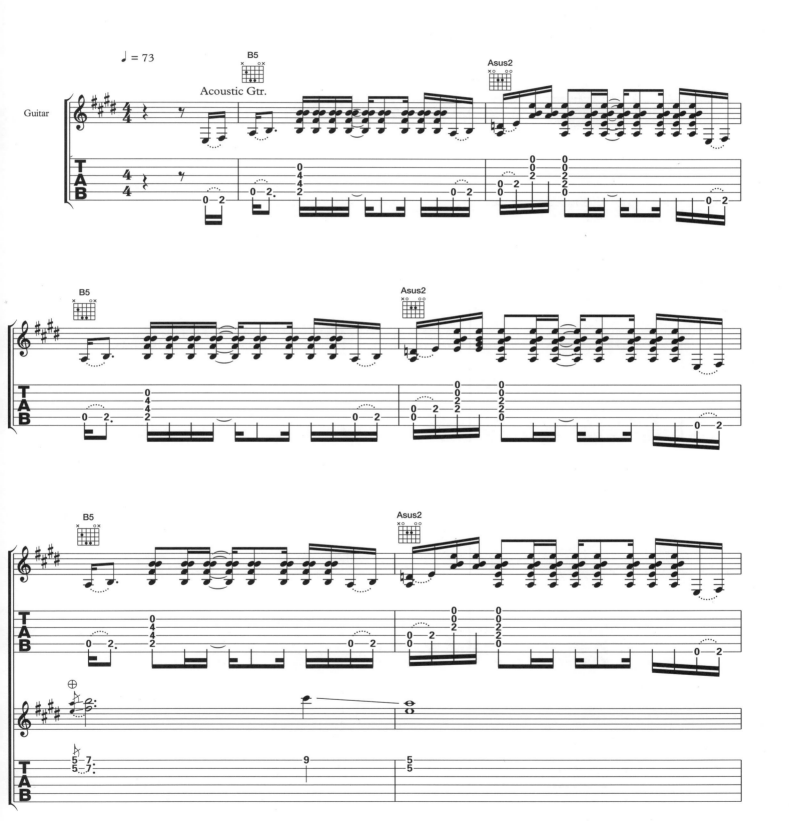

1. Here comes_____ the breeze,_____ come on, blow me up.__
2. Here come_____ the air,_____ come on, blow me up.__

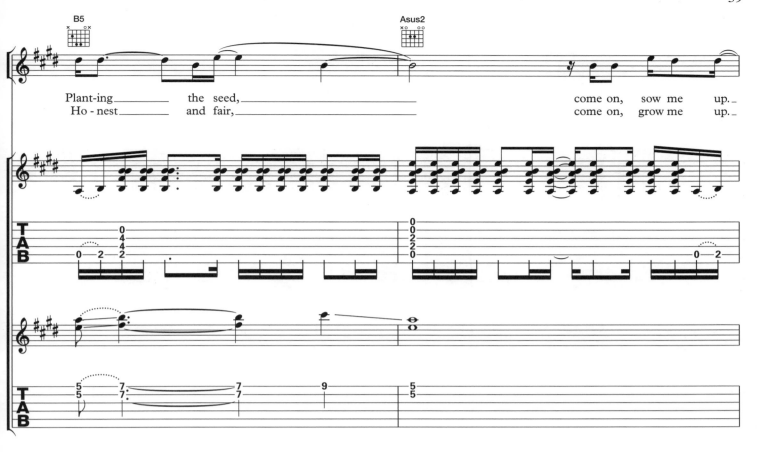

Plant-ing ___ the seed, ___ come on, sow me up. __
Ho - nest ___ and fair, ___ come on, grow me up. __

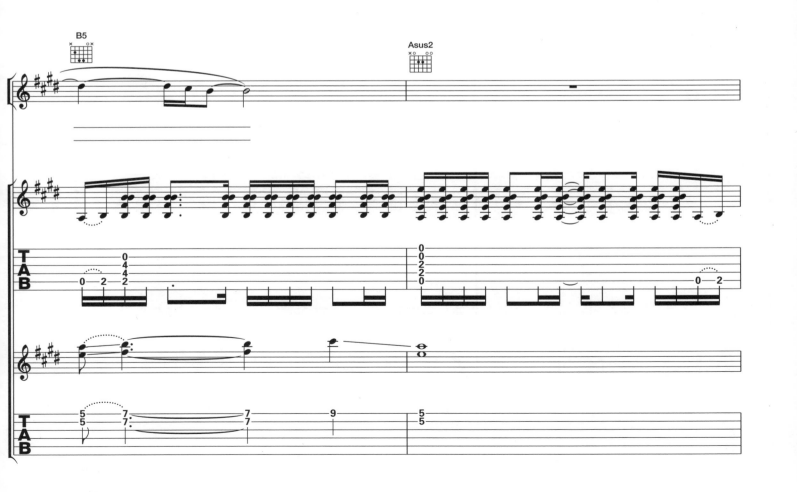

Feel - in' the feel - in',___ mak - ing our way_____ through the storm.
Star - in' at no - thin' 'cos I can't make out_____ what it is.

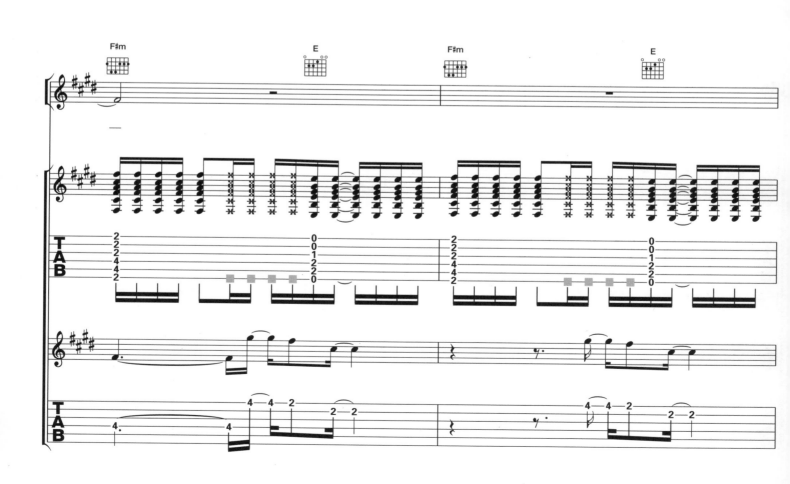

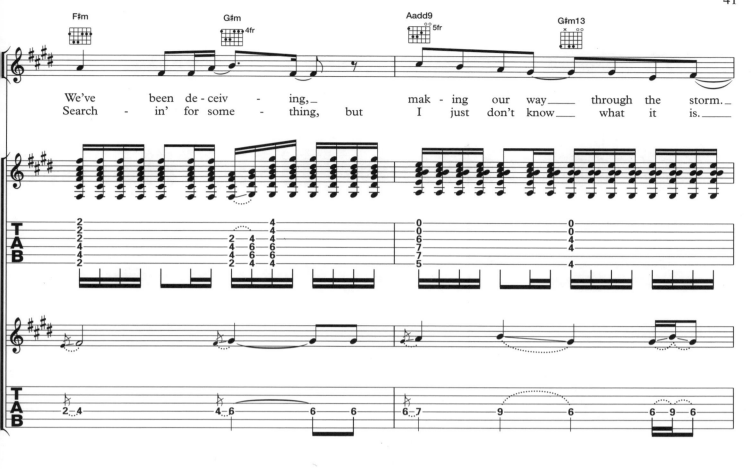

We've been de - ceiv - ing, __ mak - ing our way __ through the storm. __
Search - in' for some - thing, but I just don't know __ what it is. __

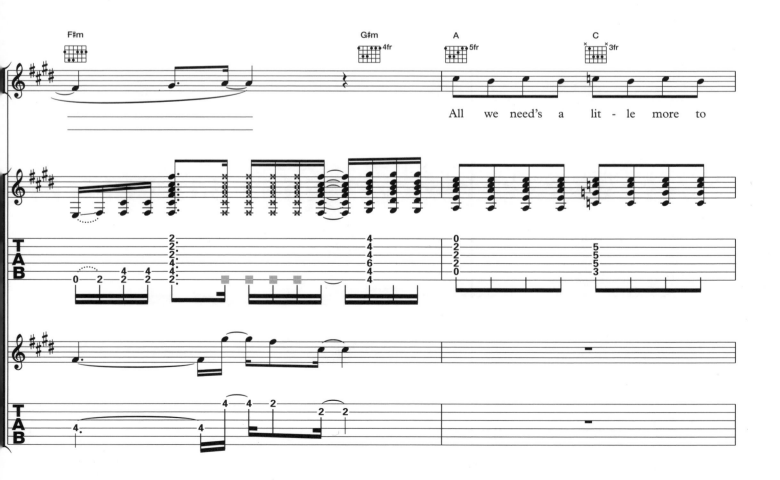

All we need's a lit - le more to

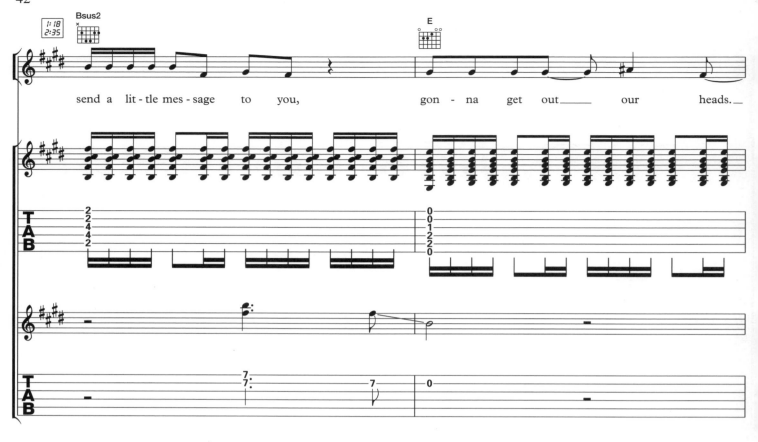

send a lit-tle mes-sage to you, gon - na get out____ our heads.____

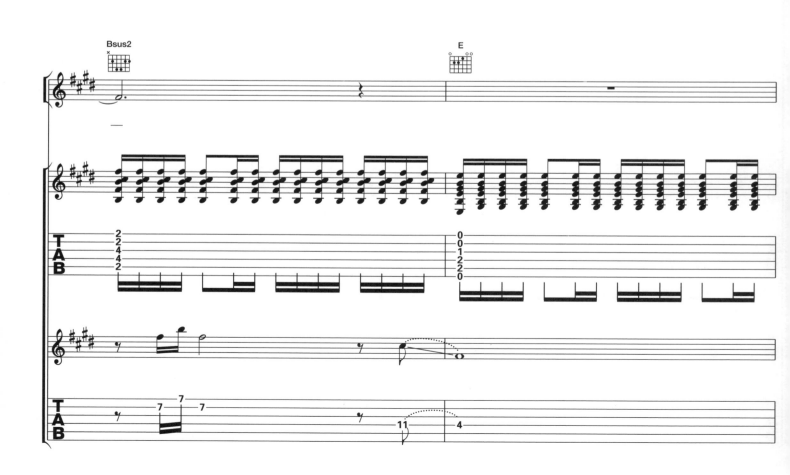

Send a lit - tle mes - sage to you, gon - na get out____ our heads.____

Well come on in,_ come on in_ and lay me down_ now. And re -

Send a lit-tle mes-sage to you, gon-na get out___ our heads.

Send a lit-tle mes-sage to you,

gon - na get out___ our heads.___

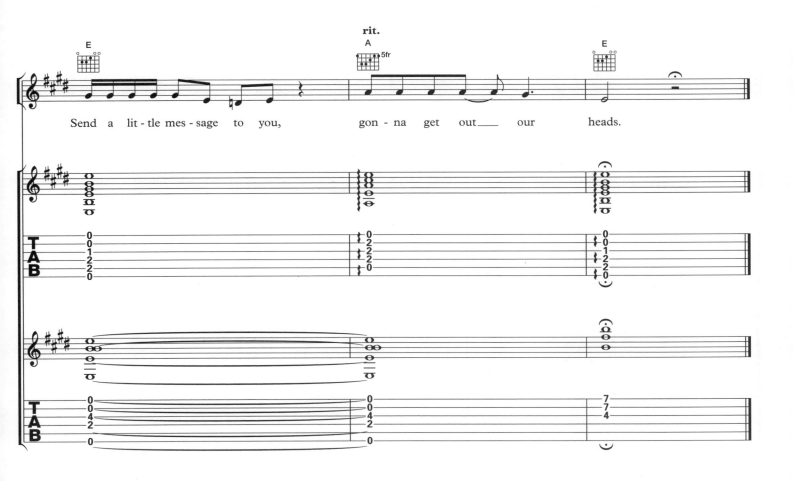

Send a lit - tle mes - sage to you, gon - na get out___ our heads.

Love Is Better Than A Warm Trombone

Words and Music by
Ian Ball, Paul Blackburn, Thomas Gray
Ben Ottewell and Oliver Peacock

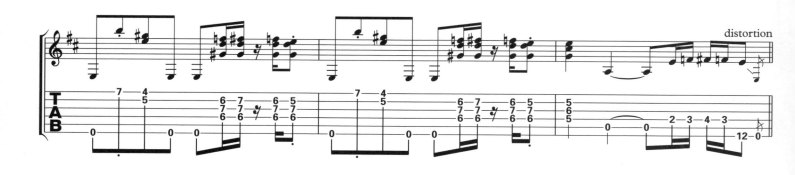

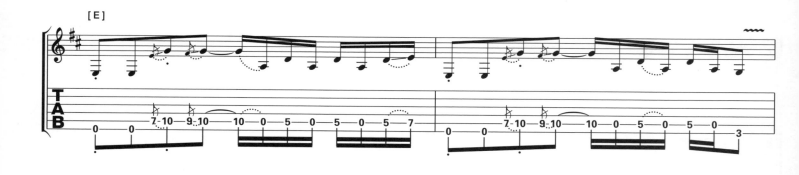

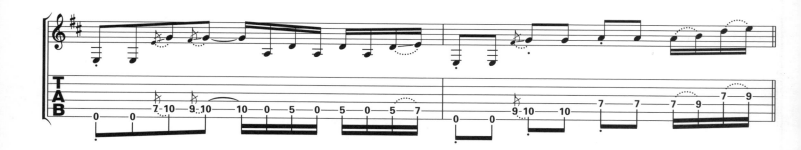

1. Love is____ bet-ter than a warm trom-bone, when blown____ soft-ly by a two tone
(2.) ri-ver_____ of__ your love-lorn soul's__ get-ting deep-er than the deep-est dish-wash-ing bowl. Now

bro-ther._____ Down on luck__ by chance, ca-ress her head off at the boog-a-loo trance. With his
bro-ther,_____ get__ the dirt off__ your hands,__ it's get-tin' dark-er than a sun-cha-ser's sun-tan.

cont. sim.

hands in his poc-ket he could not___ lie._____   With his
Hands in his poc-ket he could not___ lie._____   With his
(3.) hands in his poc-ket he be - gan to___ cry._____   With his

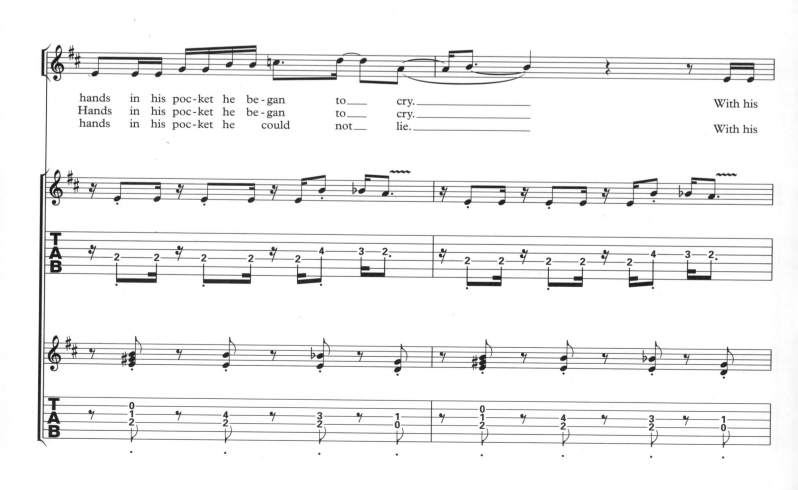

hands in his poc-ket he be-gan to___ cry._____   With his
Hands in his poc-ket he be-gan to___ cry._____   With his
hands in his poc-ket he could not___ lie._____   With his

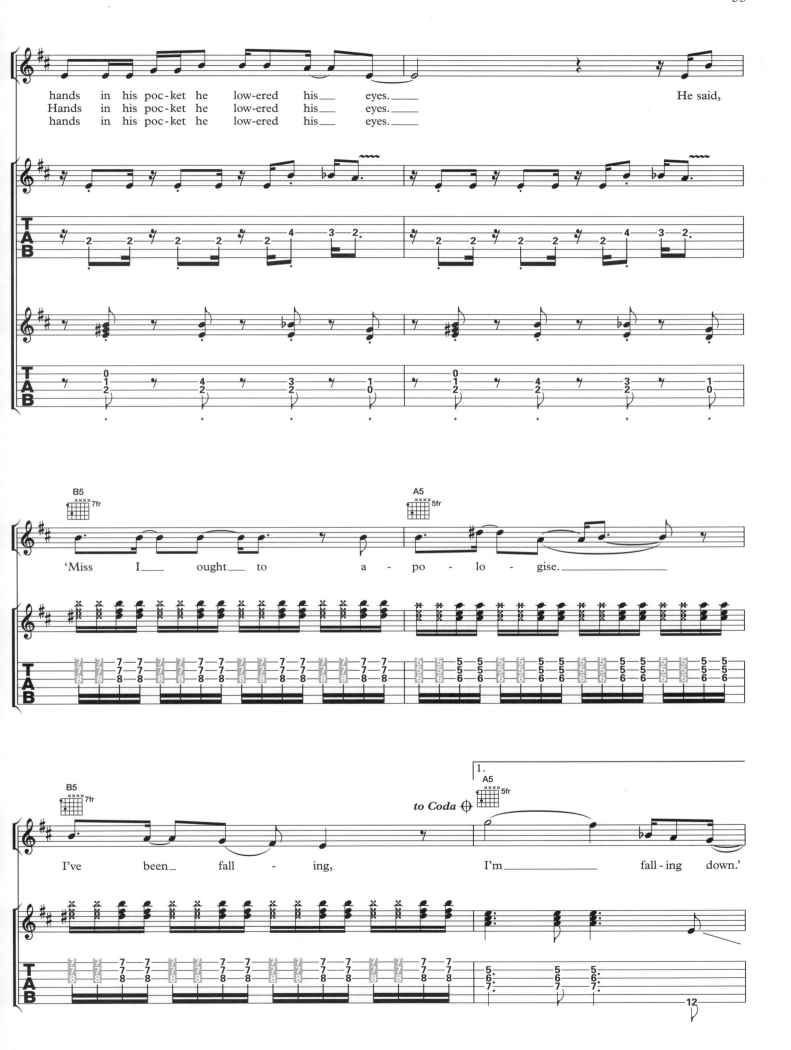

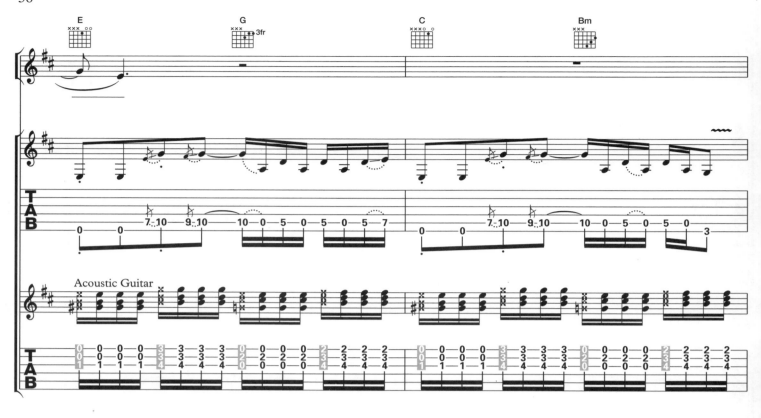

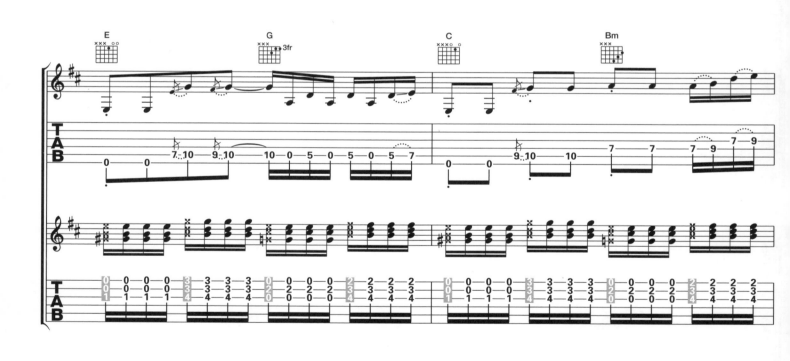

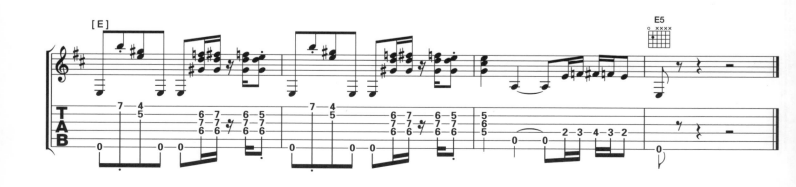

Get Myself Arrested

Words and Music by
Ian Ball, Paul Blackburn, Thomas Gray
Ben Ottewell and Oliver Peacock

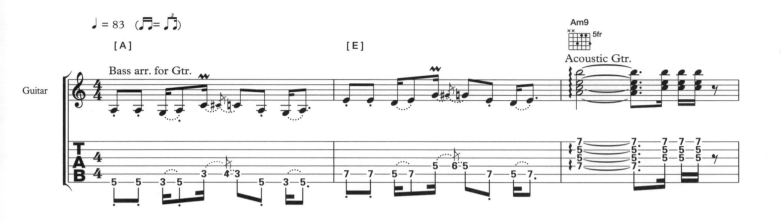

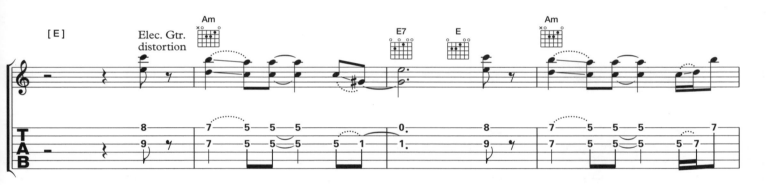

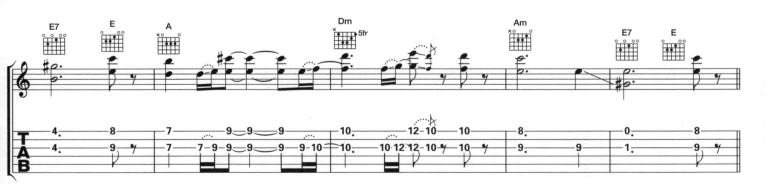

Got no time for the self - ish me and you's, tryin' a get my - self ar - rest - ed.

Free To Run

Words and Music by
Ian Ball, Paul Blackburn, Thomas Gray
Ben Ottewell and Oliver Peacock

1. I am

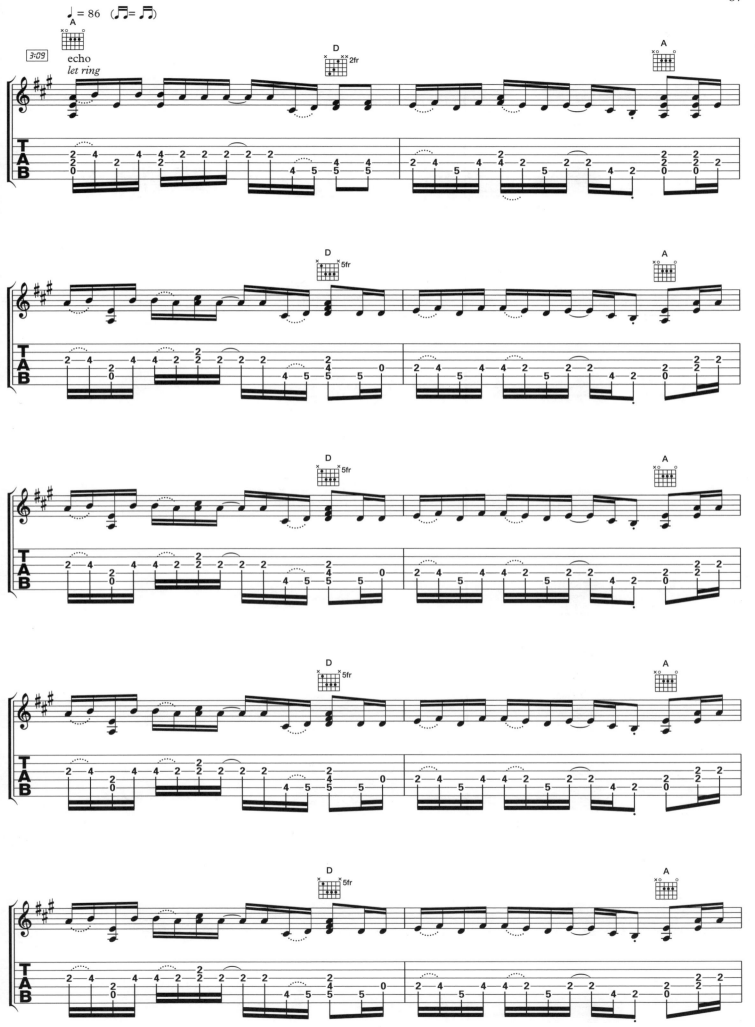

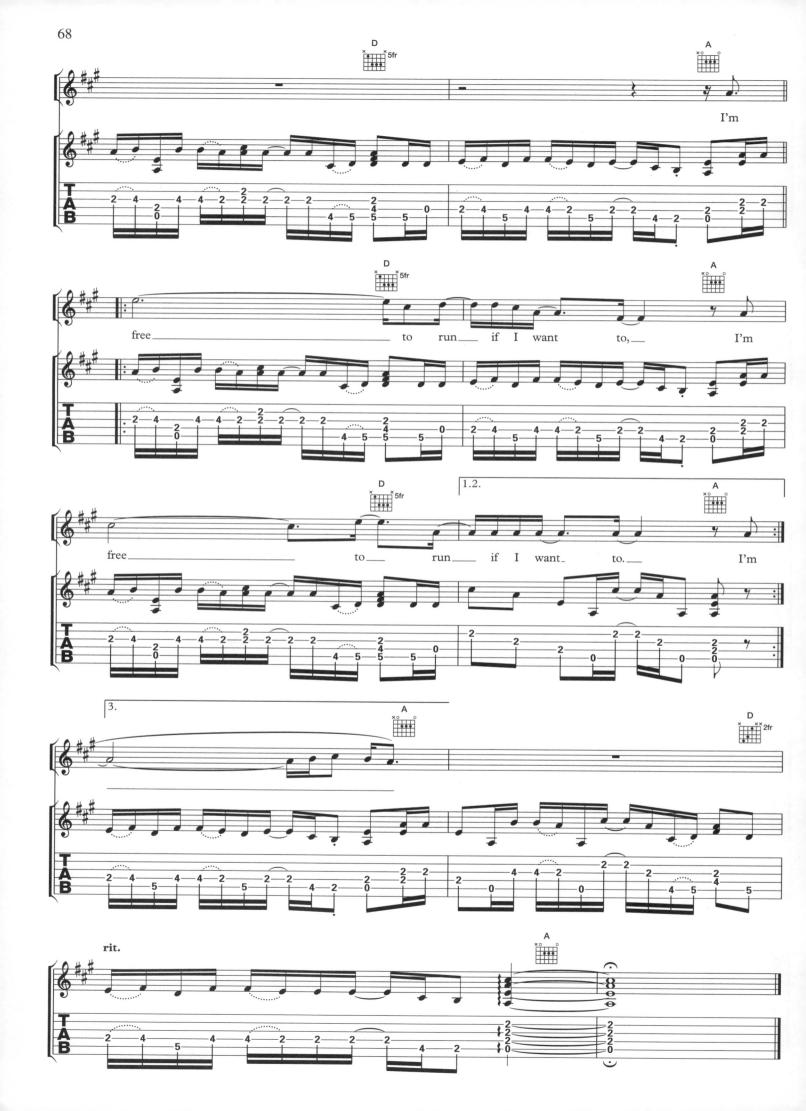

Bubble Gum Years

Words and Music by
Ian Ball, Paul Blackburn, Thomas Gray
Ben Ottewell and Oliver Peacock

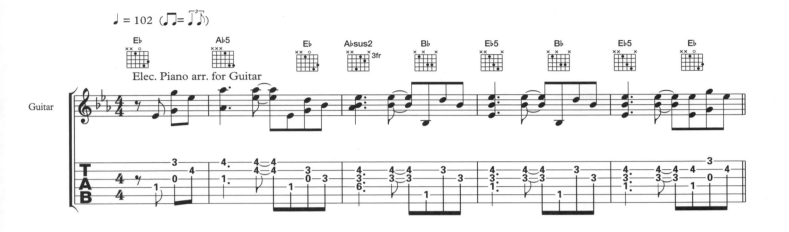

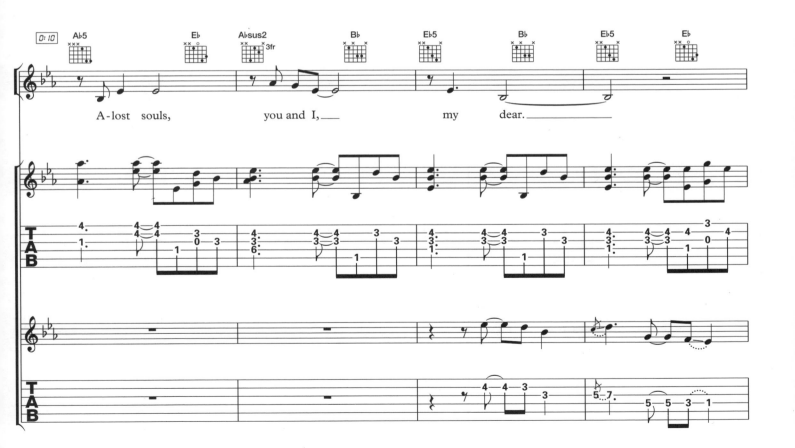

A-lost souls,   you and I,___   my   dear._____

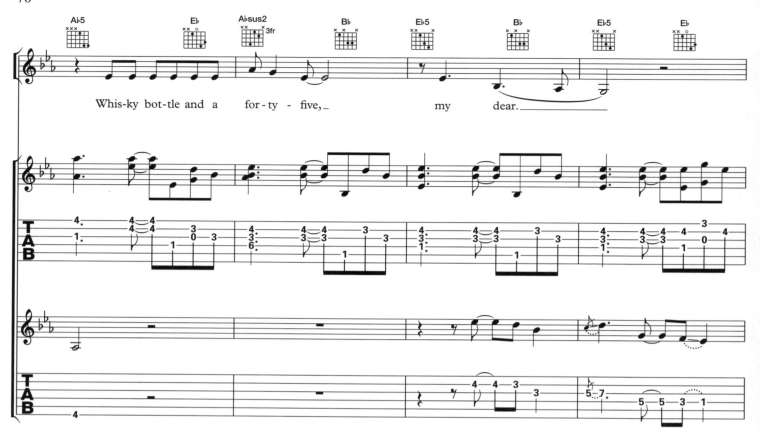

Whis-ky bot-tle and a for-ty - five,__ my dear._____

We're on a roll, suit-case and_ cel-lo-phane,___ my__ dear._____

Rie's Wagon

Words and Music by
Ian Ball, Paul Blackburn, Thomas Gray
Ben Ottewell and Oliver Peacock

1. Gon-na

take that me-di-cine, a-cold, cold me-di-cine, make me what I am. Gon-na go down stea-dy, gon-na get my mea-sure, I got

cre-dit with the medi-cine man. *Said I'm on fire,* I'm on fire.

Rie's car___ run - nin' me ov - er,___ but I don't___ mind.___ Rie's car___ driv - in' me home- ward,___ 'cos I don't___ drive.___

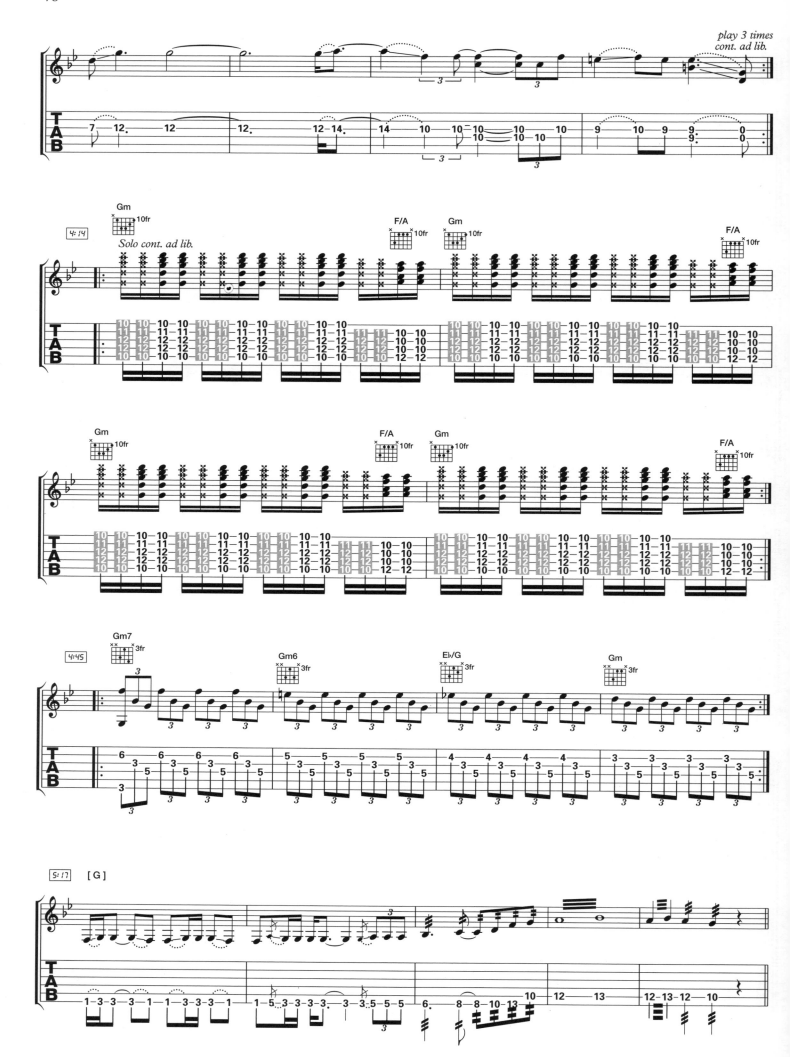

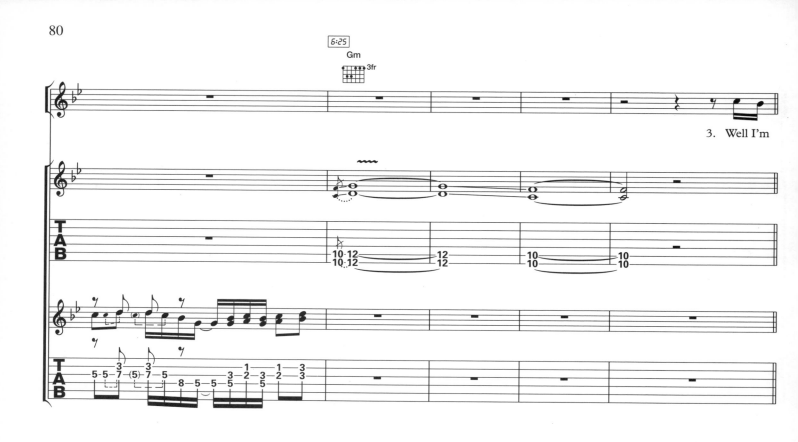

3. Well I'm

smok-ing in bed a-gain, I did-n't get the sign that said I should be up by ten.__ Gon-na

Bass arr. for Guitar

go down stea-dy, gon-na get my mea-sure, I got cre-dit with the med-i-cine man. *Said I'm on fire,*__ I'm on fire.

The Comeback

Music by
Ian Ball, Paul Blackburn, Thomas Gray
Ben Ottewell and Oliver Peacock

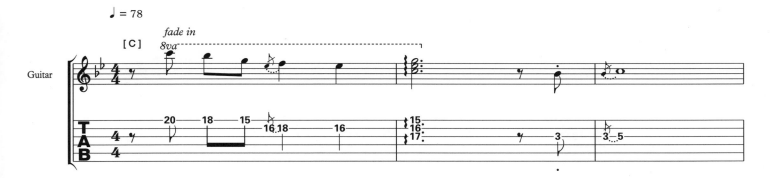

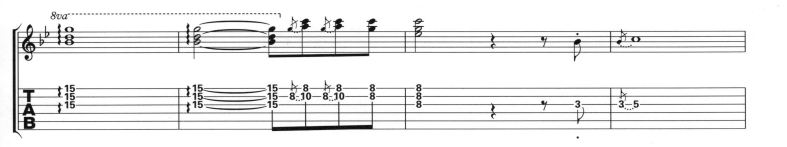

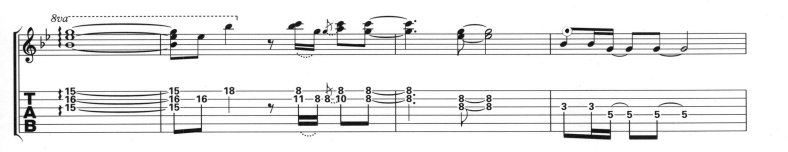

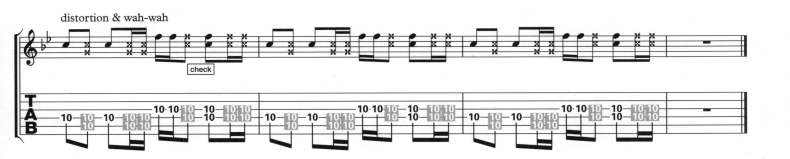

Notation and Tablature Explained

Open C chord

Scale of E major

High E (1st) string
B (2nd) string
G (3rd) string
D (4th) string
A (5th) string
Low E (6th) string

Bent Notes

The note fretted is always shown first. Variations in pitch achieved by string bending are enclosed within this symbol ⌐ ¬. If you aren't sure how far to bend the string, playing the notes indicated without bending gives a guide to the pitches to aim for. The following examples cover the most common string bending techniques:

Example 1
Play the D, bend up one tone (two half-steps) to E.

Example 4
Pre-bend: fret the D, bend up one tone to E, then pick.

Example 2
Play the D, bend up one tone to E then release bend to sound D. Only the first note is picked.

Example 5
Play the A and D together, then bend the B-string up one tone to sound B.

Example 3
Fast bend: Play the D, then bend up one tone to E as quickly as possible.

Example 6
Play the D and F♯ together, then bend the G-string up one tone to E, and the B-string up a semitone to G.

Additional guitaristic techniques have been notated as follows:

Tremolo Bar
Alter pitch using tremolo bar. Where possible, the pitch to aim for is shown.
a) Play the G; use the bar to drop the pitch to E.
b) Play the open G; use the bar to 'divebomb', i.e. drop the pitch as far as possible.

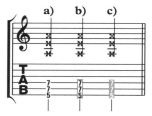

Mutes
a) Right hand mute
Mute strings by resting the right hand on the strings just above the bridge.
b) Left hand mute
Damp the strings by releasing left hand pressure just after the notes sound.
c) Unpitched mute
Damp the strings with the left hand to produce a percussive sound.

Hammer on and Pull off
Play first note, sound next note by 'hammering on', the next by 'pulling off'. Only the first note is picked.

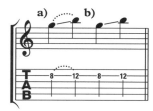

Glissando
a) Play first note, sound next note by sliding up string. Only the first note is picked.
b) As above, but pick second note.

Natural Harmonics
Touch the string over the fret marked, and pick to produce a bell-like tone. The small notes show the resultant pitch, where necessary.

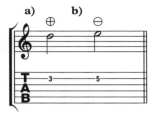

Slide Guitar
a) Play using slide.
b) Play without slide.

Artificial Harmonics
Fret the lowest note, touch string over fret indicated by diamond notehead and pick. Small notes show the resultant pitch.

Vibrato
Apply vibrato, by 'shaking' note or with tremolo bar. As vibrato is so much a matter of personal taste and technique, it is indicated only where essential.

Pinch Harmonics
Fret the note as usual, but 'pinch' or 'squeeze' the string with the picking hand to produce a harmonic overtone. Small notes show the resultant pitch.

Pick Scratch
Scrape the pick down the strings – this works best on the wound strings.

Microtones
A downwards arrow means the written pitch is lowered by less than a semitone; an upwards arrow raises the written pitch.

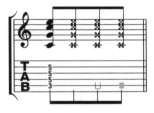

Repeated Chords
To make rhythm guitar parts easier to read the tablature numbers may be omitted when a chord is repeated. The example shows a C major chord played naturally, r/h muted, l/h muted and as an unpitched mute respectively.

Special Tunings
Non-standard tunings are shown as 'tuning boxes'. Each box represents one guitar string, the leftmost box corresponding to the lowest pitched string. The symbol '•' in a box means the pitch of the corresponding string is not altered. A note within a box means the string must be re-tuned as stated. For tablature readers, numbers appear in the boxes. The numbers represent the number of half-steps the string must be tuned up or down. The tablature relates to an instrument tuned as stated.

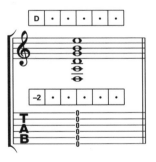

Tune the low E (6th) string down one tone (two half-steps) to D.

Chord naming
The following chord naming convention has been used:

Where there is no appropriate chord box, for example when the music consists of a repeated figure (or riff) the tonal base is indicated in parenthesis: [C]

Where it was not possible to transcribe a passage, the symbol ∿ appears.

Indications sur la notation musicale et les tablatures

Accord de Do majeur ouvert

Gamme de Mi majeur

Mi aigu: 1ère corde
Si: 2e corde
Sol: 3e corde
Ré: 4e corde
La: 5e corde
Mi grave: 6e corde

Bending

La note correspondant à la case sur laquelle on pose le doigt est toujours indiquée en premier. Les variations de hauteur sont obienues en poussant sur la corde et sont indiquées par le symbole: ⌐ ¬. En cas de doute sur la hauteur à atteindre, le fait de jouer les notes indiquées sans pousser sur la corde permet de trouver ensuite la bonne hauteur. Les examples suivants démontrent les techniques de bending les plus courantes.

Exemple 1
Jouez la note Ré et poussez la corde d'un ton (deux demi-tons) pour atteindre le Mi.

Exemple 4
'Pre-bend': posez le doigt sur la case de Ré, poussez d'un ton pour atteindre le Mi avant de jouer la note.

Exemple 2
Jouez le Ré, poussez sur la corde pour atteindre le Mi un ton plus haut, relâchez ensuite pour revenir au Ré. Seule la première note est jouée avec le médiator.

Exemple 5
Jouez La et Ré simultanément; poussez ensuite sur la corde de Si pour atteindre la note Si.

Exemple 3
'Fast Bend': jouez le Ré et poussez le plus rapidement possible pour atteindre le Mi.

Exemple 6
Jouez Ré et Fa# simultanément; poussez la corde de Sol d'un ton vers le Mi, et la corde de Si d'un demi-ton vers le Sol.

D'autres techniques de guitare sont notées de la façon suivante:

Emploi du levier de vibrato
Modifiez la hauteur du son avec le levier de vibrato. Lorsque c'est possible, la note à atteindre est indiquée.
a) Jouez le Sol et appuyez sur le levier de vibrato pour atteindre le Mi.
b) Jouez un Sol à vide et détendez le plus possible la corde avec le levier de vibrato pour rendre un effect de 'bombe qui tombe' (divebomb).

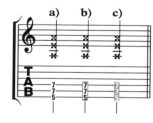

Mutes (étouffements)
a) Mute de la main droite
Etouffez en posant la main droite sur les cordes, au-dessus du chevalet.
b) Mute de la main gauche
Relâchez la pression sur la corde juste après avoir joué la note.
c) Mute sans hauteur définie
Etouffez les cordes avec la main gauche pour obtenir un son de percussion.

Hammer On et Pull Off
Jouez la première note; frappez la corde sur la touche (Hammer On) pour obtenir la seconde note, et relâchez la seconde note en tirant sur la corde (Pull Off) pour obtenir la troisième note. Seule la première note est done jouée avec le médiator.

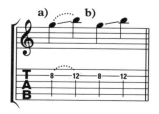

Glissando
a) Jouez la première note avec le médiator, faites sonner la seconde note en ne faisant que glisser le doigt sur la corde.
b) Comme ci-dessus, mais en attaquant également la seconde note avec le médiator.

Harmoniques naturelles
Posez le doigt sur la corde au dessus de la barrette indiquée, et jouez avec le médiator pour obtenir un son cristallin. Le cas échéant, une petite note indique la hauteur du son que l'on doit obtenir.

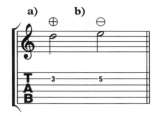

Guitare Slide
a) Note jouée avec le slide.
b) Note jouée sans le slide.

Harmoniques artificielles
Posez le doigt (main gauche) sur la note la plus basse: effleurez la corde avec l'index de la main droite au-dessus de la barrette indiquée par la note en forme de losange, tout en actionnant le médiator. La petite note indique la hauteur du son que l'on doit obtenir.

Effet de Vibrato
Jouez le vibrato soit avec le doigt sur la corde (main gauche), soit avec le levier de vibrato. Comme le vibrato est une affaire de technique et de goût personnels, il n'est indiqué que quand cela est vraiment nécessaire.

Harmoniques pincées
Appuyez le doigt sur la corde de la façon habituelle, mais utilisez conjointement le médiator et l'index de la main droite de façon á obtenir une harmonique aiguë. Les petites notes indiquent la hauteur du son que l'on doit obtenir.

Scratch
Faites glisser le médiator du haut en bas de la corde. Le meilleur effet est obtenu avec des cordes filetées.

Quarts de ton
Une flèche dirigée vers le bas indique que la note est baissée d'un quart-de-ton. Une flèche dirigée vers le haut indique que la note est haussée d'un quart-de-ton.

Accords répétés
Pour faciliter la lecture des parties de guitare rythmique, les chiffres de tablature sont omis quand l'accord est répété. L'example montre successivement un accord de Do majeur joué de façon normale, un 'mute' de la main droite, un 'mute' de la main gauche et un 'mute' sans hauteur définie.

Accordages spéciaux
Les accordages non-standards sont indiqués par six cases, chacune représentant une corde (de gauche à droite), de la plus grave à la plus aiguë. Un tiret indique que la tension de la corde correspondante ne doit pas être altérée. Un nom de note indique la nouvelle note à obtenir. Pour les tablatures, les chiffres indiqués dans les cases représentent le nombre de demi-tons dont ou doit désaccorder la corde, vers le haut ou vers le bas.

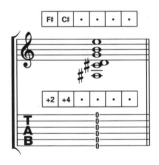

Accordez la corde de Mi grave un ton plus haut de façon à obtenir un Fa#, et la corde de La deux tons plus haut de façon à obtenir un Do#.

Noms des accords

Lorsqu'aucun nom d'accord précis n'est applicable, par exemple quand la musique consiste en une figure répétée (riff), le centre tonal est indiqué entre parenthèses: **[C]**

Lorsqu'un passage n'a pas pu être transcrit, le symbole ～ apparait.

Hinweise zu Notation und Tabulatur

Offener C - Dur - Akkord

E - Dur - Tonleiter

Hohe E-Saite (1.)
H-Saite (2.)
G-Saite (3.)
D-Saite (4.)
A-Saite (5.)
Tiefe E-Saite (6.)

Gezogene Noten

Die gegriffene Note wird immer zuerst angegeben. Das Zeichen ⌐ ¬ zeigt eine Veränderung der Tonhöhe an, die durch das Ziehen der Saiten erreicht wird. Falls Du nicht sicher bist, wie weit die Saite gezogen werden soll, spiele die entsprechenden Töne zunächst ohne Ziehen; so kannst Du Dich an der Tonhöhe orientieren. Die folgenden Beispiele geben die gebräuchlichsten Techniken zum Ziehen wieder:

Beispiel 1
Spiele das D und ziehe dann um einen Ton (zwei Halbtonschritte) höher zum E.

Beispiel 4
Im Voraus gezogen: Greife das D, ziehe um einen Ton höher zum E und schlage erst dann die Saite an.

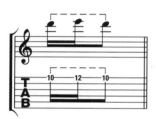

Beispiel 2
Spiele das D, ziehe um einen Ton hoch zum E und dann wieder zurück, so daß D erklingt. Dabei wird nur die erste Note angeschlagen.

Beispiel 5
Spiele A und D gleichzeitig und ziehe dann die H-Saite um einen Ton nach oben, so daß H erklingt.

Beispiel 3
Schnelles Ziehen: Spiele das D und ziehe dann so schnell Du kannst um einen Ton höher zum E.

Beispiel 6
Spiele D und Fis gleichzeitig; ziehe dann die G-Saite um einen Ton nach oben zum E und die H-Saite um einen Halbtonschritt nach oben zum G.

Zusätzliche Spieltechniken für Gitarre wurden folgendermaßen notiert:

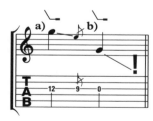

Tremolo
Verändere die Tonhöhe mit dem Tremolo-Hebel. Wenn es möglich ist, wird die angestrebte Tonhöhe angezeigt.
a) Spiele G; nutze den Takt, um zum E abzusteigen.
b) Spiele die leere G-Saite; nutze den Takt, um so weit wie möglich abzusteigen.

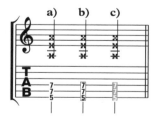

Dämpfen
a) Mit der rechten Hand
Dämpfe die Saiten, indem Du die rechte Hand einfach oberhalb der Brücke auf die Saiten legst.
b) Mit der linken Hand
Dämpfe die Saiten, indem Du den Druck der linken Hand löst, kurz nachdem die Töne erklingen.
c) Ohne bestimmte Tonhöhe
Dämpfe die Saiten mit der linken Hand; so erzielst Du einen 'geschlagenen' Sound.

Hammer on und Pull off
Spiele die erste Note; die zweite erklingt durch 'Hammering on', die dritte durch 'Pulling off'. Dabei wird nur die erste Note angeschlagen.

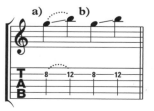

Glissando
a) Spiele die erste Note; die zweite erklingt durch Hochrutschen des Fingers auf der Saite. Nur die erste Note wird angeschlagen.
b) Wie oben, aber die zweite Note wird angeschlagen.

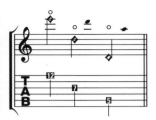

Natürliches Flageolett
Berühre die Saite über dem angegebenen Bund; wenn Du jetzt anschlägst, entsteht ein glockenähnlicher Ton. Wo es nötig ist, zeigen kleine Notenköpfe die entstandene Note an.

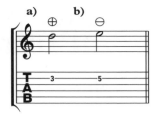

Slide Guitar
a) Spiele mit Rutschen des Fingers.
b) Spiele ohne Rutschen.

Künstliches Flageolett
Greife die unterste Note, berühre die Saite über dem durch Rauten angegebenen Bund und schlage dann den Ton an. Die kleinen Notenköpfe zeigen wieder die entstandene Note an.

Vibrato
Beim Vibrato läßt Du die Note für die Dauer eines Tons durch Druckvariation oder Tremolo-Hebel 'beben'. Da es jedoch eine Frage des persönlichen Geschmacks ist, wird Vibrato nur dort angegeben, wo es unerläßlich ist.

Gezupftes Flageolett
Greife die Note ganz normal, aber drücke die Saite mit der zupfenden Hand so, daß ein harmonischer Oberton entsteht. Kleine Notenköpfe zeigen den entstandenen Ton an.

Pick Scratch
Fahre mit dem Plektrum nach unten über die Saiten – das klappt am besten bei umsponnenen Saiten.

Vierteltöne
Ein nach unten gerichteter Pfeil bedeutet, daß die notierte Tonhöhe um einen Viertelton erniedrigt wird; ein nach oben gerichteter Pfeil bedeutet, daß die notierte Tonhöhe um einen Viertelton erhöht wird.

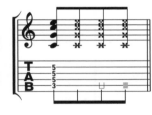

Akkordwiederholung
Um die Stimmen für Rhythmus-Gitarre leichter lesbar zu machen, werden die Tabulaturziffern weggelassen, wenn ein Akkord wiederholt werden soll. Unser Beispiel zeigt einen C - Dur - Akkord normal gespielt, rechts gedämpft, links gedämpft und ohne Tonhöhe.

Besondere Stimmung
Falls eine Stimmung verlangt wird, die vom Standard abweicht, wird sie in Kästchen angegeben. Jedes Kästchen steht für eine Saite, das erste links außen entspricht der tiefsten Saite. Wenn die Tonhöhe einer Saite nicht verändert werden soll, enthält das Kästchen einen Punkt. Steht eine Note im Kästchen, muß die Saite wie angegeben umgestimmt werden. In der Tabulaturschrift stehen stattdessen Ziffern im entsprechenden Kästchen: Sie geben die Zahl der Halbtonschritte an, um die eine Saite höher oder tiefer gestimmt werden soll.

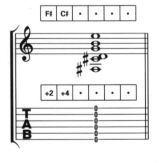

Stimme die tiefe E-Saite (6.) um einen Ganzton (zwei Halbtonschritte) höher auf Fis und die A-Saite (5.) um zwei Ganztöne (vier Halbtonschritte) höher auf Cis.

Akkordbezeichnung
Die folgenden Akkordbezeichnungen wurden verwendet.

Wenn kein eigenes Akkordsymbol angegeben ist, z.B. bei Wiederholung einer musikalischen Figur (bzw. Riff), steht die Harmoniebezeichnung in Klammern: [C]

Das Symbol ~ steht jeweils dort, wo es nicht möglich war, einen Abschnitt zu übertragen.

Spiegazione della notazione e dell'intavolatura

Accordo di Do aperto
(in prima posizione)

Scala di Mi maggiore

Mi acuto: la corda
Si: 2a corda
Sol: 3a corda
Re: 4a corda
La: 5a corda
Mi basso: 6a corda

Bending

La prima nota scritta è sempre quella tastata normalmente. Le alterazioni di altezza da realizzare con la trazione laterale della corda (bending) interessano le note comprese sotto al segno: ⌐￢. Se siete incerti sull'entità dell'innalzamento di tono da raggiungere, suonate le note indicate tastando normalmente la corda. Gli esempi seguenti mostrano le tecniche più comunemente impiegate nella maggior parte dei casi che possono presentarsi.

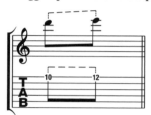

Esempio 1
Suonate il Re e innalzate di un tono (due mezzi toni) a Mi.

Esempio 2
Suonate il Re, tirate alzando di un tono a Mi e rilasciate tornando a Re. Va suonata solo la prima nota.

Esempio 3
'Bend Veloce': suonate il Re e quindi alzate di un tono a Mi il più velocemente possibile.

Esempio 4
'Pre-Bend': tastate il Re, tirate alzando di un tono a Mi e poi suonate.

Esempio 5
Suonate simultaneamente La e Si quindi tirate la 2a corda per innalzare il suono a Si.

Esempio 6
Suonate simultaneamente Re e Fa# quindi tirate la 3a corda alzando il suono di un tono a Mi, e la 2a corda di mezzo tono, alzando il suono a Sol.

Negli esempi seguenti sono illustrate altre tecniche chitarristiche:

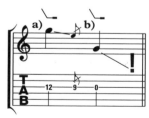

Barra del tremolo
Alterate l'altezza del suono mediante la barra del tremolo. Dove possibile l'altezza da raggiungere è indicata.
a) Suonate il Sol e abbassate il suono fino a Mi mediante la barra.
b) Suonate il Sol a vuoto e scendete quanto più possibile.

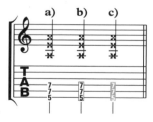

Smorzato
a) **Smorzato con la destra**
Smorzare le corde con il palmo della mano destra in prossimità del ponticello.
b) **Smorzato con la sinistra**
Smorzare le corde allentando la pressione delle dita subito dopo aver prodotto i suoni.
c) **Pizzicato**
Premere leggermente le corde in modo che non producano note ma soltanto un effetto percussivo.

Legature ascendenti e discendenti
Suonate la prima nota e ricavate la seconda percuotendo la corda con il dito contro la barretta; per la terza nota tirate la corda con il medesimo dito. Soltano la prima nota va suonata.

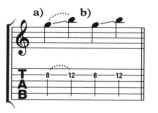

Glissando
a) Suonate la prima nota e ricavare la seconda facendo scivolare il dito lungo la corda. Va pizzicata solo la prima nota.
b) Come sopra, ma pizzicando anche la seconda nota.

Armonici naturali

Toccate leggermente la corda sulla barretta indicata e pizzicate col plettro per produrre un suono di campana. Le notine indicano il suono risultante, dove occorra.

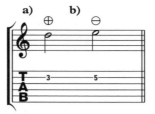

Slide Chitarra

a) Suonare con slide.
b) Suonare senza slide.

Armonici artificiali

Tastate la nota più bassa, toccate leggermente la corda sulla barretta relativa alla nota romboidale e pizzicate con il plettro. Le notine indicano il suono risultante.

Vibrato

Effettuate il vibrato facendo oscillare il dito che preme la corda oppure con la barra del tremolo. Poichè il vibrato è un fatto di gusto personale, viene indicato solo dove è essenziale.

Armonici pizzicati

Tastate normalmente la nota ma pizzicate la corda con la mano destra per ricavare l'armonico sopracuto. Le notine indicano l'altezza del suono risultante.

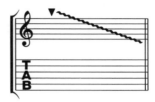

Suono graffiato

Fate scorrere il bordo del plettro lungo la corda. L'effetto è maggiore sulle corde fasciate.

Microintervalli

Una freccia diretta verso il basso significa che il suono scritto va abbassato di un intervallo inferiore al semitono; una freccia diretta verso l'alto innalza il suono scritto.

Accordi ripetuti

Per facilitare la lettura, possono venire omessi i numeri nell'intavolatura di un accordo ripetuto. L'esempio mostra un accordi di Do maggiore suonato normalmente, smorzato con la destra, smorzato con la sinistra e pizzicato (muto).

Accordature Speciali

Le accordature diverse da quella normale sono indicate in speciali 'gabbie di accordatura'. Ogni gabbia rappresenta una corda di chitarra; all'estremità sinistra corrisponde la corda più bassa. Il simbolo '•' in una gabbia sta ad indicare che l'intonazione della corda corrispondente è quella normale. Una nota nella gabbia indica che l'intonazione di quella corda va modificata portandola all'altezza indicata. Per coloro che leggono l'intavolatura, dei numeri posti nelle gabbie stanno ad indicare di quanti semitoni deve salire o scendere l'intonazione della corda. L'intavolatura è da considerarsi relativa ad uno strumento accordato come indicato nelle gabbie.

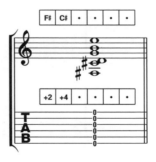

Accordate la corda del Mi basso (6a) un tono sopra (due semitoni) a Fa#.
Accordate la corda del La basso (5a) due toni sopra (quattro semitoni) a Do#.

Indicazione degli accordi

E' stata impiegata la seguente nomenclatura convenzionale degli accordi.

Quando non compare la griglia appropriata di un accordo, ad esempio, quando la musica consiste nella ripetizione di una stessa figura (riff), la base tonale è indicata fra parentesi: [C]

Dove non è stato possibile trascivere il passaggio, compare il segno ～.

Printed in England
The Panda Group · Haverhill · Suffolk · 5/99